# The Adventures of
# Hot Cocoa and Salt Water Taffy

## Searching for a Forever Family

To Charlotte and Mickey

Marla Beagle

Written by
**Marla Beagle**

Illustrated by
**Joan Critz Limbrick**

The Adventures of Hot Cocoa and Salt Water Taffy

ISBN 978-0-9989781-0-9

Copyrighted by Hartwood Pet Lodge LLC 2017
All rights reserved
Published by Hartwood Pet Lodge LLC
www.Hartwoodpetlodge.com

First Edition

Illustrations are watercolor and mixed media on 300 lb. Arches watercolor paper.
Text is Gill Sans MT. Illustrations, graphic and cover design is by Joan Critz Limbrick.
joan@joanlimbrick.com

Printed in the USA by Worzalla Publishing

www.Hartwoodpetlodge.com

# Searching for a Forever Family

Dedicated to Mom and Dad.
It all started with Pierre.

Hi, my name is Hot Cocoa...
but my friends call me Cocoa for short.
Would you like to be my friend?

I'm going to board a train and search for a Forever Family. You can come too! Would you like to travel with me, Taffy?

I sure would like to go with you, Cocoa!
I don't have a family either so count me in!

Together we will have a fun adventure, Taffy.

But how will we know when we find a Forever Family, Cocoa?

We'll know it!
We'll be hugged all-day-long, and we'll feel so special and so loved.

**Such a long train ride! I am so hungry...**
**Is that barking I hear, Taffy?**

***Cocoa, I think I see dogs over there...***

Yes, you do! It's an animal shelter, Taffy.
Let's prance over there and meet those dogs.

Gee, Cocoa! They sure are friendly dogs.
Oh no...it's starting to rain!

Let's follow the pack inside, Taffy.
I hope there's an extra bedroom for us.

Cocoa, this room is perfect!
Let's settle down and spend time with our new friends.

*Dinner was so yummy that I licked my bowl clean!*
*Cocoa...how will we ever find our Forever Family?*

**Don't worry, Taffy. Tomorrow we board a plane to continue our search.**

Good night and sleep tight my friend,
Hot Cocoa.

Sweet dreams to you my friend,
Salt Water Taffy.

Here we go, up-up and away!
Are you daydreaming, Taffy?

*Yes, Cocoa. I'm dreaming of the day when I meet my Forever Family.*

STAFFORD REGIONAL AIRPORT

POODLE TAXI

**What a nice welcome! Taffy, follow me!
It's time to jump into this Poodle Taxi!**

*I wonder where we'll be going next, Cocoa?*

*I've never ridden in a poodle taxi, Cocoa. This is cool!*

Yikes, Taffy! Those three big poodles must live here.
They look like they want to play with us.

I'm ready to play too, Cocoa. Are you?

I hope we can keep up with their fast paws, Taffy.
One, two, three, here we go!

Good morning
and guess what, Taffy!

A family has found you!
A poodle named Teddy, who
lives in a nearby, town wants
you to be his brother!

And guess what else?

I have a family now too!
I will be staying here with
Asa, Rita and Marla, the
three big poodles.

*But I will miss you, Hot Cocoa.*

I will miss you too, Salt Water Taffy.
But don't worry...friends forever always stay in touch.

Teddy is here! It is time for me
to join my Forever Family.

Thank you for asking me to
travel with you, Cocoa.
It sure was a fun adventure!

Goodbye for now, Salt Water Taffy.
Remember, we are friends forever!

DEAR TAFFY,

I AM SO GLAD WE BOTH
FOUND FOREVER FAMILIES.
MY FAMILY MAKES ME FEEL
SO SPECIAL! THANK YOU
FOR TRAVELING WITH ME.

　　LOVE,
　　　HOT COCOA

P.S. FRIENDS FOREVER

Dear Cocoa,

I feel special too! I am hugged all-day-long and feel so loved. I love my forever family.

Love from your friend forever,
          Salt Water Taffy

# THE REAL LIFE POODLES IN THIS STORY

TAFFY

TEDDY

COCOA

MARLA

ASA

RITA

# MORE ABOUT HOT COCOA AND SALT WATER TAFFY'S
## REAL-LIFE ADVENTURE

During Cocoa and Taffy's adventure, they were helped by many dedicated people who arranged and provided temporary lodging in North Carolina and air transportation to Fredericksburg, Virginia. *Throughout the United States, many non-profit animal rescue organizations and shelters provide food, bedding, exercise, and health care for animals waiting to be adopted or being transportation to other locations where adoptions are possible.*

Cocoa and Taffy traveled over 1,000 miles starting in central Texas, a temporary stay in North Carolina, and their final stop in Fredericksburg, Virginia. They flew in a small privately-owned airplane and landed at Stafford Regional Airport, Stafford County, Virginia on July 3, 2015. *Animals searching for temporary or permanent families are most often transported by automobiles, but airplanes also transport as well.*

Cocoa and Taffy were fostered for one month before being adopted by their Forever Families. *When food, shelter, and medical care are provided for a dog on a temporary basis, this caretaking process is called fostering, and the dog is referred to as the foster-dog.*

Cocoa and Taffy are miniature poodles. *Miniature poodles means that they are not the smallest nor the largest sized-poodles. Poodles are bred in three sizes: toy (small), miniature (medium), and standard (large). A poodle's size is determined by their height not their weight. Measuring from the withers (the ridge between the shoulder blades) to the floor level determines size. A toy poodle is 10" or under from the withers to the floor. A miniature poodle is greater than 10" and including 15" from the withers to the floor. A standard poodle is greater than 15" from the withers to the floor.*

Cocoa and Taffy's hair colors are different from one another. *Cocoa's hair color is called café-au-lait and Taffy's hair is white. Poodles are bred in many colors like white, silver, black, cream, apricot, café-au-lait, and brown.*

Cocoa and Taffy live in Virginia with their Forever Families.
*Cocoa lives in Hartwood, Virginia with Marla, Rita, and Asa. Taffy lives with Teddy in Fairfax County, Virginia.*

# YOUR DOG'S CARE AND SAFETY

Provide daily exercise for your dog.

Always provide clean drinking water for your dog.

Provide a bed/area specifically for your dog to relax and sleep.

Never leave your dog unattended in an automobile at any time.

Do not allow your dog to extend their head or any other body
part from an automobile or other means of transportation.

Visit your neighborhood veterinarian (animal doctor) yearly for your dog's checkup and required vaccinations.

Always maintain control of your dog with a leash connected to their collar or harness, and attach an
identification tag with your family's current contact information. An identification chip inserted under
your dog's skin, performed by a veterinarian, is another means of identification to safeguard your dog.

Secure your dog while being transported in a car or other mode of transportation. Use dog crates
or dog seat belts. (While flying from North Carolina to Virginia, and riding in the poodle taxi to
their foster home, Cocoa and Taffy were safely crated).

Dogs require regular washing and brushing (called grooming). Certain breeds require haircuts
and additional grooming needs. Ask your neighborhood professional groomer for assistance.

Your dog wants to spend time with you. Take time daily to show your dog how much you
love them. Hug them all-day-long, and you will make them feel so special and so loved!
They will love YOU in return!

## THANK YOU

Thank you to my big-hearted husband who always welcomes animals into our home. Thank you, Don and Tota, for welcoming Taffy into your family. Thank you to all the incredibly caring people who gave their time and resources to help Cocoa and Taffy find their forever families. Thank you to the Stafford Junction children who read to Cocoa, Marla, Rita and Asa during Summer Junction Day Camp 2016 Fredericksburg, Virginia; your love for our poodles inspired me to share Cocoa and Taffy's story. Most of all, thank you, Joan, for answering my telephone call and making this true dog story come alive through your fantastic artwork.

A portion from each book sale will be donated to a nonprofit animal rescue organization.

To buy books in bulk, contact Marla Beagle:
poodletaxi@gmail.com

The Real Poodle Taxi

## ABOUT THE AUTHOR
## Marla Beagle

Carol McElhaney Shelton, aka Marla Beagle, grew up in Yacht Haven Estates, Alexandria, Virginia, with her first Standard Poodle named Pierre. Marla and her husband have shared their home over the years with 13 poodles of various sizes and an English Setter. Dedicated to the rescue of dogs like Salt Water Taffy and Hot Cocoa, they work to transport, shelter and locate Forever Families. Located on their property, Hartwood Pet Lodge LLC is a quiet and loving place for dogs to stay while they search for their Forever Families.

www.Hartwoodpetlodge.com

## ABOUT THE ARTIST
## JOAN CRITZ LIMBRICK

Joan lives and works from her studio in the country near Fredericksburg, Virginia. She is a freelance illustrator and graphic designer, as well as a painter, potter, poet and an author of several children's books. Her life is never boring.

www.joanlimbrick.com